CW00656069

BRAIN TEASERS
FOR SMART ENGINEERS

Tricky Brain Twisters, Mind Games, and Fun Problem Solving for Engineers

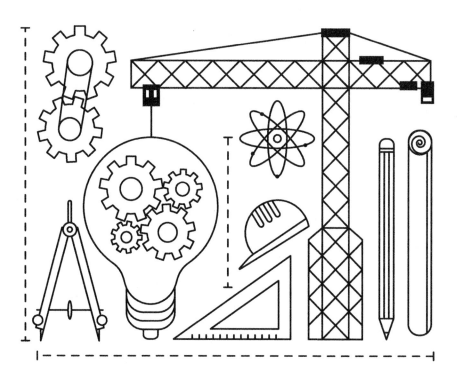

IQ Street

ISBN: 979-8-89095-044-4
Copyright © 2024 By Curious Press
ALL RIGHTS RESERVED

No part of this book may be reproduced, stored in a retrieval system, or transmitted in any form or by any means, electronic, mechanical, photocopying, recording, scanning, or otherwise without the prior written permission of the publisher.

The illustrations in this book were designed using images from Freepik.com.

CONTENTS

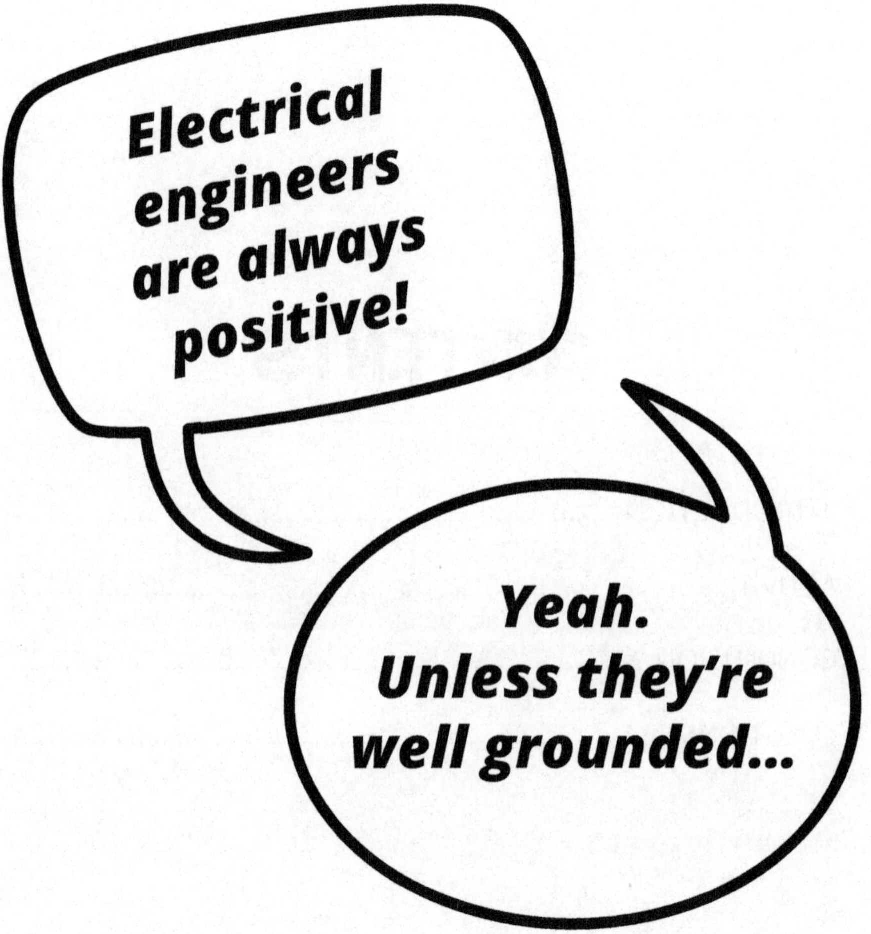
Electrical engineers are always positive!
Yeah. Unless they're well grounded...

INTRODUCTION

Where would the world be without engineering?

It's safe to say practically everything we do and interact with throughout the day will, at some point, have been designed, tested, approved, or constructed by an engineer.

It might be something as small as sending a text message or making a cup of coffee, or something as large as crossing a bridge, driving a car, or boarding a train on our commute to work. The world and the work of engineering—including mathematics, geometry, the physical sciences, and everything else this grand subject entails—is all around us, every single day.

If you're an engineer, of course, then you'll already know just how important and how influential an industry it is. You will also very likely have a keen mind and a sharp problem-solving brain on your shoulders, perfect for spotting flaws, making improvements, and just generally ensuring everything around us works as it should. So how about we give that keen puzzle-solving mind of yours a little workout?

This is **BRAIN TEASERS FOR SMART ENGINEERS**. Inside here, you'll find 100 fun puzzles, games, and tricky activities all designed to test your problem-solving skills to their limits.

This isn't just your normal puzzle book, however. The focus here is squarely on games and puzzles that will tax an engineer's brain in particular—so we're going to spend the next 100 pages or so building, solving, drawing, transforming, and unscrambling our way through some very fiendish games.

Instead of your standard quick crossword puzzles, for instance, here you're going to be faced with skeleton crosswords—in which you not only have to solve the clues but also build the games as you go!

Instead of your standard picture puzzles and games, you're going to be tasked with inverting, upscaling, and otherwise transforming an array of tricky images.

And instead of simply unscrambling word jumbles, here you're going to be given number codes to crack and cryptograms to solve.

Don't worry if your super-smart brain hits the odd stumbling block along the way, though. If ever you need a hint—or you've come to a dead end and just need to see how to proceed! —you can turn to the back of the book for full solutions and explanations of all the puzzles included here.

And finally, don't worry if that all sounds a little intense! Along the way here, we have plenty of japes, jokes, quotes, aphorisms, and witty one-liners to keep you entertained and give your mind a quick break.

So let's get started, shall we? Grab a pen or a pencil, kick back, and let's find out just what these puzzles are all about ...

BRAIN TEASERS FOR SMART ENGINEERS

"This current situation is shocking!"

This first puzzle is a skeleton crossword.

Here, you have to answer the ACROSS and DOWN clues, just as in an ordinary crossword puzzle. But as well as solving the clues, you'll also need to build the grid as you go—including all the black squares—and figure out from there where each answer goes!

To help you, some of the clue numbers and black squares have been placed in the grid already.

Remember, crosswords like these have rotational symmetry—so if there is a black square four spaces in from the left on the second row down (as there is here!), then there must be a corresponding black square four spaces in from the right on the second row from the bottom to match it. So you can go ahead and fill that box in now!

Remember, too, that unless an ACROSS answer starts in the very first column, there must be a black space in front of it. Likewise, unless a DOWN answer starts in the top row, each of those answers must have a black square in front of them as well.

So, with all of that in mind, can you build this puzzle using the clues below and the grid on the opposite page?

ACROSS

1. Seller's demand
9. Device establishing an internet connection
10. Southern African country
11. Engrave
12. Defensive canine
14. Light-hearted stage comedies
15. Collection of cups and saucers
18. Laughing harshly, like a witch
20. Scots dynasty
22. Soothing song for a child
23. Selects
24. Hopeless task

DOWN

2. Motorcycle attachment
3. Stressed and unstressed syllable pairing
4. Very intelligent person
5. Commented
6. Multiplied a digit by its square
7. In a flawed or unsound manner
8. Disobedience
13. Punish severely
16. Semiconducting element 14, used in electric circuits
17. Catalyst
19. Large stringed instrument
21. Spiked wheel on a rider's boot

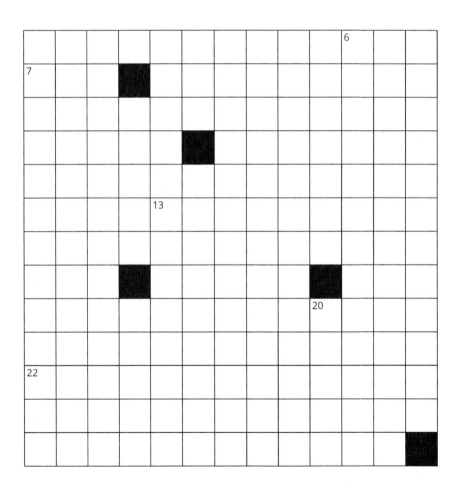

Another type of puzzle you'll come across in this book is this one—a classic sudoku puzzle.

To complete a sudoku grid, you need to fill out each row, column, and smaller 3x3 square of 9 cells with the digits 1–9. However, there can be no repeats—each number must only appear once in each row, column, and 3x3 square.

Based on the digits already placed in the grid, see if you can complete this puzzle.

4	2	3		9		8	7	
8	1		2	3	6	9	5	4
			8			3	1	2
2		8	4		7	1		
			6	2	1		8	
1	5	4	9	8		2	6	
	4	5					9	
		2	3		8	5	4	1
			5	4	9	7		

This is a transformation puzzle. Take a look at the grid of shapes and symbols below.

In the empty grid beneath it, you must recreate the same pattern rotated 90° counter-clockwise. Remember, you'll not only need to rotate the positions of the symbols, but some of the symbols themselves will not look the same when turned around.

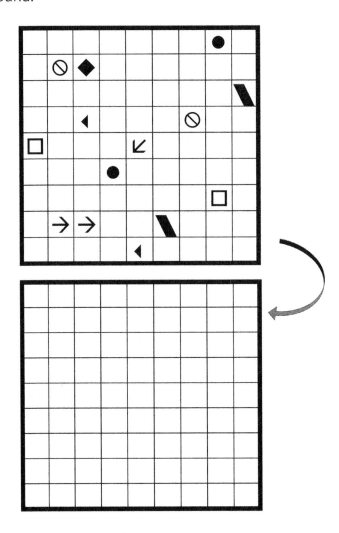

4

This is a directions game. Each of the squares below contains a number and a directional instruction, telling you how many squares to move next, and in which direction.

Starting in the box containing the only two-digit multiple of 3 higher than 50, follow the chain of directions until you reach one of the shaded squares in the center of the grid.

What is the first shaded letter you land in at the end of the chain—A, B, C, or D?

98 2 RIGHT	6 1 LEFT	37 3 DOWN	16 4 DOWN	14 1 DOWN	7 4 DOWN	55 2 DOWN	61 3 DOWN	77 4 DOWN
10 1 UP	17 4 DOWN	23 1 DOWN	50 3 DOWN	**A**	19 1 LEFT	24 2 DOWN	62 7 LEFT	11 4 LEFT
18 1 DOWN	52 3 RIGHT	103 3 RIGHT	37 1 RIGHT	**B**	4 5 LEFT	76 2 LEFT	44 1 RIGHT	25 2 DOWN
28 3 DOWN	17 2 DOWN	31 1 DOWN	13 4 RIGHT	**C**	51 4 LEFT	9 5 LEFT	40 1 RIGHT	37 1 DOWN
42 1 RIGHT	2 1 UP	14 4 RIGHT	21 3 LEFT	**D**	3 1 LEFT	20 2 RIGHT	6 6 LEFT	44 3 UP
32 1 UP	6 5 RIGHT	41 1 RIGHT	22 3 LEFT	34 1 UP	101 1 UP	28 1 RIGHT	19 4 UP	67 4 LEFT

5

You've been out for a walk and just checked your pedometer, which tells you that you have walked 8,008 steps today. How many more steps will you have to walk today to reach the next palindromic number?

6

Rotating the number 6 by 180° turns it into the number 9—an increase of 50% on the original value. What single-digit number has the largest percentage increase in numerical value when rotated through just 90°?

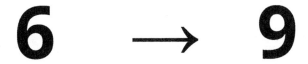

*"There are 10 types of people in the world.
Those who understand binary, and those who don't."*

7

This is a crisscross game. All these terms from the world of robotics connect together in the grid below. Can you find the correct home for each one?

ARTICULATION

BASE LINK

COMPUTER AIDED DESIGN

CYCLE

DEBUGGER

DEGREES OF FREEDOM

ELECTRICAL

FLEXURE

FORCE FEEDBACK

FRAME

GANTRY

LINEAR MOTION

RISK

SAFEGUARD

SEGMENT

SENSOR

SERVO

YAW

How many squares in total can you see in the figure below?

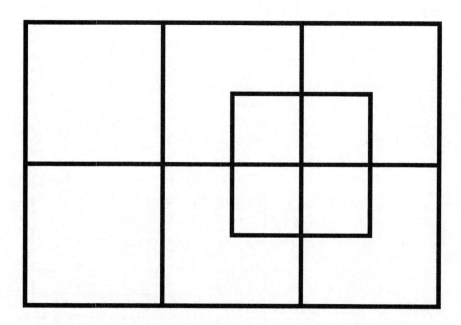

Did you know?

The word *geometry* comes from two Greek roots literally meaning "measuring the earth"!

Reading from left to right, from one row onto the next, the five sets of symbols and boxes below follow a sequence. Which of the six boxes from the bottom of the page should come next in the sequence?

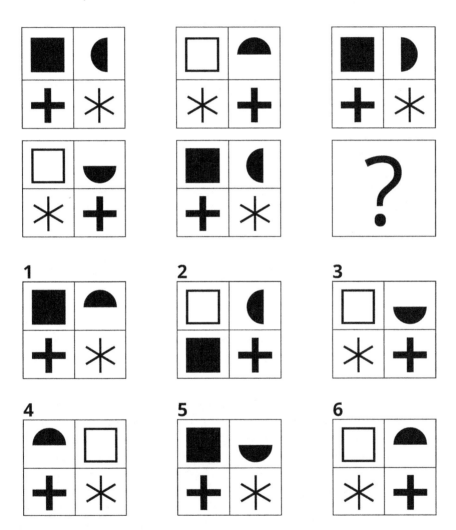

This is a logic puzzle. Using the clues and the grid on the next page, can you figure out the answer to this four-way problem?

Four mechanics—Bob, Craig, Gary, and Phil—have worked on four very different vehicles this week. One worked on a sports car; another on a monster truck; a third on a motorcycle; and the fourth on a school bus. And each vehicle was on a different day.

Based on the clues below, can you work out who worked on what and when? The first clue has been filled in the grid already to show you how to solve this puzzle—and be sure to use the checklist grid at the bottom of the next page as you go.

1. Gary worked on the bus, but not on Friday.
2. The unusual vehicle Bob worked on was the appointment he attended on Wednesday.
3. Craig's first appointment of the week on Monday was mending an engine problem on a sports car!
4. The monster truck did not suffer its mechanical failure on Wednesday.

	Sports car	Monster truck	Motorcycle	School bus	Monday	Tuesday	Wednesday	Friday
Bob				✗				
Craig				✗				
Gary	✗	✗	✗	✓				✗
Phil				✗				
Monday				
Tuesday				
Wednesday				
Friday				✗

MECHANIC	VEHICLE	DAY
Bob		
Craig		
Gary	School bus	
Phil		

11

Time for another sudoku puzzle. Can you complete this grid so that the digits 1–9 appear once and only once in each row, each column, and each smaller 3x3 square of cells?

7			8					
9		1		3	5			8
5	2				4	1		
1	9				7	8	3	
				1		5		
3			9			2		4
6		9		8			4	7
4	1		5			6	8	
	8	7	3	4	6			

Did you know?

Tin is the only chemical element with a 3-letter name.

12

Can you work your way through this maze from the opening at the top to the toolkit on the other side?

"Did you hear about the engineering teacher who had to leave the class?
He was feeling a bit ANSI."

Time to test your brainpower and wordpower with another skeleton crossword.

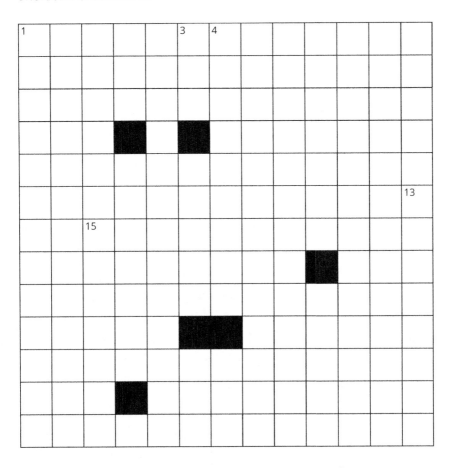

ACROSS: 1. Ice hockey disc **3.** Give an account of **9.** Exterior **10.** Birds' homes **11.** Autonomy **14.** Pen lid **16.** Fissure **17.** Her **18.** Without stopping **21.** Publicity **22.** Television station **23.** Riches **24.** Require

DOWN: 1. State, region **2.** Quoted, referenced **4.** Make a mistake **5.** Normal, regular **6.** Bugs **7.** Facile **8.** Creative works **12.** Manmade fabric, synthetic polymer **13.** Used again **15.** Ask to marry **19.** From the point at which **20.** Zit **22.** Automobile

Take a look at the grid of shapes and symbols below. In the empty grid beneath it, you must recreate the same pattern rotated 90° clockwise. Remember, you'll not only need to rotate the positions of the symbols, but some of the symbols themselves will not look the same when turned around.

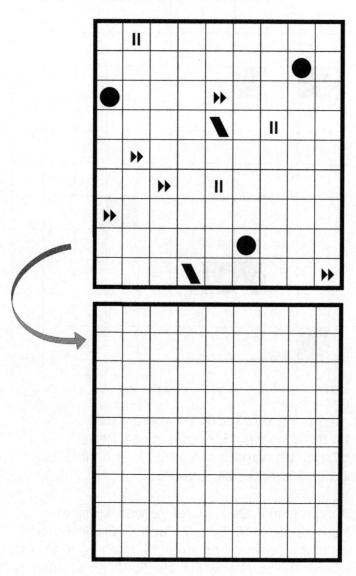

15

You have **(A)** a flask containing oil at 15°C and **(B)** a flask containing pure water at 25°F.

If you were to drop an iron ball into both flasks, in which flask would the ball travel the slowest and take the longest time to reach the bottom?

A Oil   **B** Water

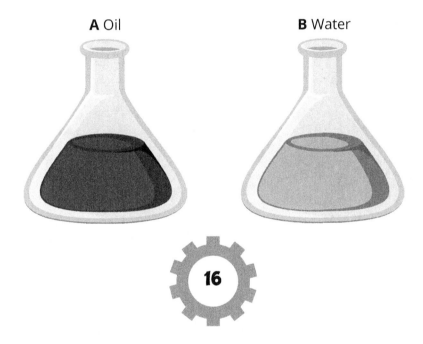

16

Look at the die below. If you were to push the die one roll backwards from the right, so that the 5 were now on top and the 6 were out of sight, and then one roll backwards from the left, so that the 4 were now on top, what number would appear where the 4 currently is in the picture?

Reading from left to right, from one row onto the next, the five sets of symbols and letters below follow a sequence. Which of the six boxes from the bottom of the page should come next in the sequence?

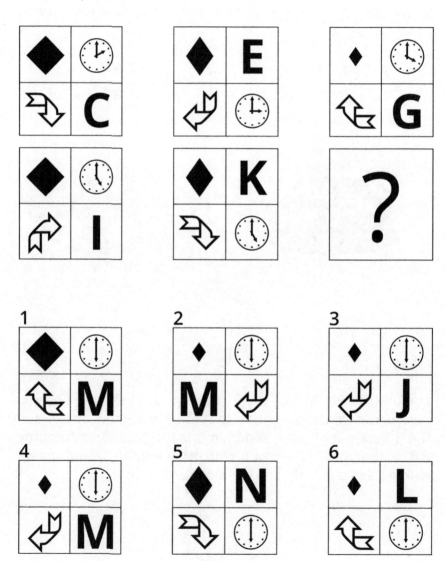

Each of the squares below contains a number and a directional instruction telling you how many squares to move next, and in which direction.

Starting in the square containing the **only multiple of 9 in the grid**, follow the chain of directions until you reach one of the shaded squares in the center of the grid.

What is the first shaded letter you land in at the end of the chain—A, B, C, or D?

11	3	32	16	92	42	37	4	37
2 RIGHT	4 DOWN	2 DOWN	4 DOWN	1 DOWN	5 DOWN	5 DOWN	1 LEFT	2 DOWN
73	**19**	**52**	**1**	**A**	**51**	**31**	**15**	**29**
4 RIGHT	6 RIGHT	2 LEFT	1 RIGHT		1 LEFT	2 LEFT	1 RIGHT	3 DOWN
78	**54**	**61**	**89**	**B**	**20**	**33**	**17**	**26**
2 RIGHT	6 RIGHT	2 RIGHT	1 LEFT		1 LEFT	3 DOWN	2 UP	2 LEFT
68	**33**	**30**	**23**	**C**	**66**	**95**	**46**	**39**
7 RIGHT	2 UP	1 LEFT	3 RIGHT		2 RIGHT	1 DOWN	6 LEFT	1 LEFT
40	**4**	**11**	**35**	**D**	**48**	**107**	**55**	**100**
4 UP	1 UP	2 UP	4 RIGHT		5 LEFT	2 UP	2 LEFT	1 LEFT
53	**38**	**22**	**2**	**24**	**82**	**10**	**94**	**20**
2 RIGHT	2 RIGHT	2 UP	1 UP	4 LEFT	2 RIGHT	4 LEFT	3 LEFT	1 LEFT

Did you hear about the person who invented the escalator?

Yes, they were mechanically inclined!

The following six numbers have been removed from the magic square below:

1   2   3   7   8   9

Can you replace the numbers in the grid so that each column and each row totals 15?

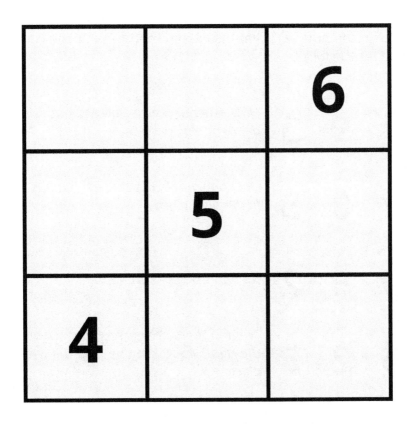

This padlock requires a 3-digit code to open it.

Some of the codes below have been tried. Based on what we know of the numbers that have been tried, what is the correct code for the lock?

7 9 3 *Only one number is correct, but it is in the right place.*

7 0 5 *Only one number is correct, but it is not in the right place.*

9 8 2 *No numbers are correct.*

5 2 3 *Two numbers are correct, and one is in the right place, but one is in the wrong place.*

8 7 4 *Only one number is correct, but it is not in the right place.*

Time for another sudoku puzzle. Can you complete this grid so that the digits 1–9 appear once and only once in each row, each column, and each smaller 3x3 square of cells?

2		4			8			
	9		2	1	7		4	
7			6				3	9
1			5	4	6			
4	3		1		9	6		
		9	8	2	3		1	
	1				2	9		
	2		7					
9			3		5	1	2	

Did you know?

The fewest possible number of clues required to solve a sudoku puzzle is 17.

We're building bridges with this next crisscross puzzle. Can you find the right home for all these bridge-building terms in the grid so that they all connect with one another?

ABUTMENT	DRAWBRIDGE	PARAPET
ARCH	EMBANKMENT	PIER
BATON	FOUNDATION	SPAN
BEARINGS	GIRDER	STRUT
CABLES	GROUND	SUSPENSION
CANITLEVER	INTEGRAL BEAM	TOWER
DECKING	KEYSTONE	TRUSS

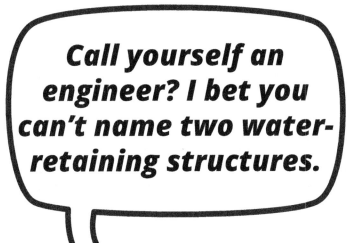

Take a look at the grid of shapes and symbols below.
In the empty grid beneath it, you must recreate the same pattern rotated 90° counter-clockwise. Remember, you'll not only need to rotate the positions of the symbols, but some of the symbols themselves will not look the same when turned around.

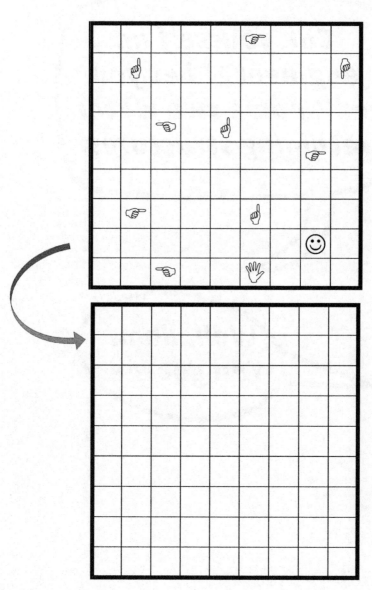

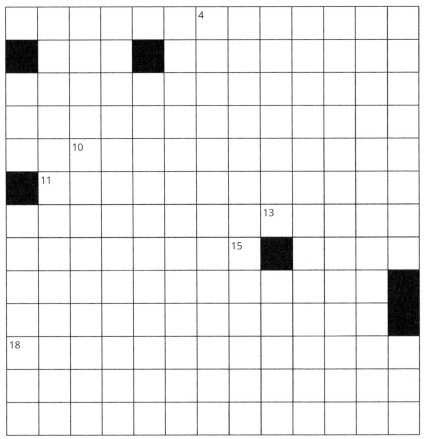

ACROSS: 1 Tell off **4** Pails **9** Candies and sweets
10 Purplish sharp-tasting fruits **12** Worry **13** Shortens a text
16 Hater of people or mankind **18** Inherently clumsy
19 Most enthusiastic **20** Spirit of an era

DOWN: 2 Circular structure, ring **3** Wide-scale removal of trees
5 As one **6** Someone who closely shares another's interests or
personality **7** Annoys, vexes **8** Smell **11** Surround on all sides
14 Capital of Greece **15** Thick soup **17** Reverse the effect of

Imagine if the flat shape below were to be made into a three-dimensional shape, as if built out of five identical cubes.

How many perfectly square faces would the three-dimensional shape have?

Did you know?

The plus sign was invented in the 16th century by a Welsh mathematician called Robert Recorde. He also introduced the equals sign!

What direction will Gear A have to be turned so that Gear B rotates clockwise?

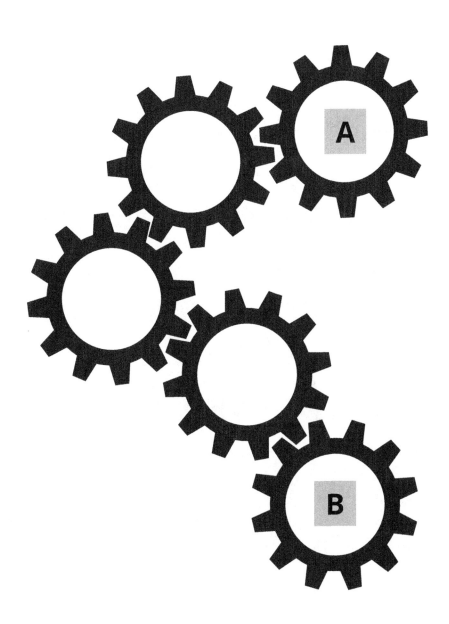

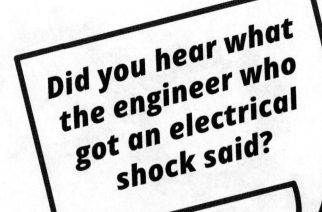

How many squares are there in this form?

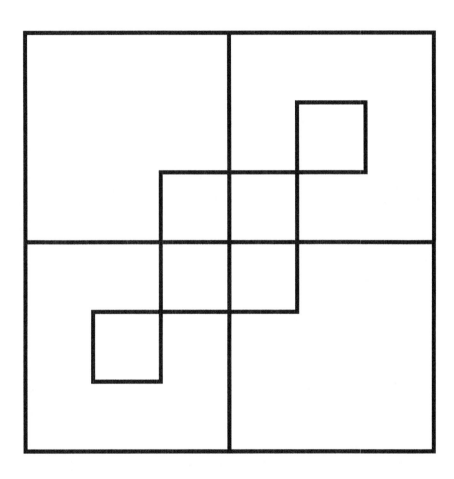

Reading from left to right, from one row onto the next, the five sets of symbols and boxes below follow a sequence. Which of the six boxes from the bottom of the page should come next in the sequence?

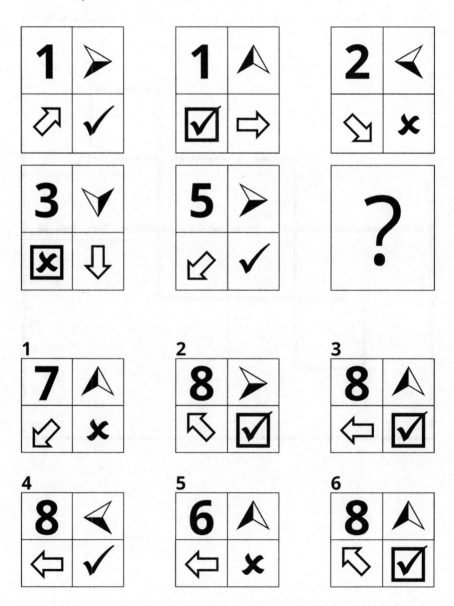

Each of the squares below contains a number and a directional instruction telling you how many squares to move next, and in which direction.

Starting in the square containing the square **one number less than 7 squared**, follow the chain of directions until you reach one of the shaded squares in the center of the grid.

What is the first shaded letter you land in at the end of the chain—A, B, C, or D?

11	7	102	22	84	43	87	55	9
6 RIGHT	2 DOWN	1 DOWN	4 RIGHT	2 RIGHT	1 DOWN	2 DOWN	4 DOWN	1 DOWN
6	**59**	**114**	**10**	**A**	**90**	**84**	**30**	**19**
4 RIGHT	2 DOWN	1 DOWN	1 UP		3 LEFT	1 DOWN	3 LEFT	2 DOWN
32	**4**	**40**	**44**	**B**	**56**	**18**	**34**	**91**
1 DOWN	2 DOWN	1 RIGHT	4 RIGHT		4 LEFT	2 DOWN	1 DOWN	3 DOWN
35	**24**	**2**	**17**	**C**	**19**	**48**	**43**	**93**
3 UP	3 RIGHT	1 RIGHT	2 UP		1 LEFT	3 LEFT	1 RIGHT	1 LEFT
23	**33**	**X**	**60**	**D**	**111**	**50**	**99**	**54**
1 DOWN	1 LEFT	X	1 RIGHT		1 DOWN	5 LEFT	1 DOWN	1 DOWN
52	**16**	**18**	**32**	**5**	**101**	**17**	**23**	**10**
4 LEFT	2 UP	1 UP	1 LEFT	1 RIGHT	2 UP	1 UP	6 LEFT	2 LEFT

Solve this substitution cipher to reveal a quote about engineering.

"QCBW QNW VWGQ QNCQ WJTGQG CEU
"___E___ ___ ____ T___ __I__S _N_

KCBW TQ VWQQWM. INWE TQ UPWG EPQ
____ __ B_____. _H___ __ ____ ____

WJTGQ, UWGTSE TW."
_____, D_____ __."

The second hand of a clock travels 360° every minute. The minute
hand of a clock travels 360° every hour. How many degrees does
the hour hand travel in 60 minutes?

"Did you hear about the frog that studied mechanical engineering?

It started saying 'Rivet! Rivet!'"

Time for another sudoku puzzle. Can you complete this grid so that the digits 1–9 appear once and only once in each row, each column, and each smaller 3x3 square of cells?

1	4		5	3				
3						7	2	4
		9	6				3	1
	6	3				2		5
9	8		2		7			3
2			8		3	9		7
5			4	2		3	7	8
6	7			9	5	4		2
4	3	2	7				5	9

Did you know?

The oldest device known as a "computer" is 2,000 years old!

It's the summer break at college and four engineering classmates—Graham, Hannah, Isaiah, and John—have arranged placement jobs for August. One of them is specializing in architecture; another in manufacturing; a third in transport; and a fourth in electrical engineering. One friend has secured a place abroad; another with his family's business; a third is working with the local council; and a fourth has a position with an agency in the next city over.

Based on the clues on the next page, can you work out who is specializing in what and where they are spending their summer?

	Architecture	Manufacturing	Transport	Electrics	Abroad	Family business	Local council	Agency
Graham								
Hannah								
Isaiah								
John								
Abroad								
Family business								
Local council								
Agency								

1. The person who will be working with their family's business is not an architect.
2. Hannah will be spending the summer abroad—but she is not the manufacturing student, and neither is Graham.
3. The names of the electrical engineer and the architect end in H.
4. The person studying transport infrastructure has a placement with the local council.
5. Isaiah is going to work for his family business.

CLASSMATE	SUBJECT	PLACEMENT
Graham		
Hannah		
Isaiah		
John		

Take a look at the grid of shapes and symbols below.
In the empty grid beneath it, you must recreate the same pattern
rotated 90° counter-clockwise. Remember, you'll not only need
to rotate the positions of the symbols, but some of the symbols
themselves will not look the same when turned around.

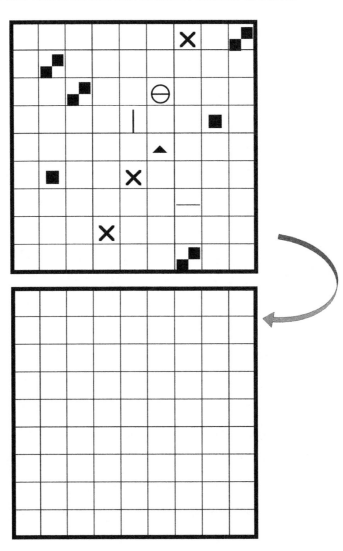

Here's a quick trio of brain teasers and riddles to wrap your brain around.

A: What timepiece has the fewest moving parts—and what timepiece has the most?

B: What is the next letter in this sequence?

M A M J J A

C: There are eleven 3-digit prime numbers between 100 and 200.

Six of them are pairs of anagrams—that is, they are made from the same three digits as another 3-digit prime number between 100 and 200. Name one of the pairs.

41, 47, 53, 59, 71, 83, 89 ... 227, 233

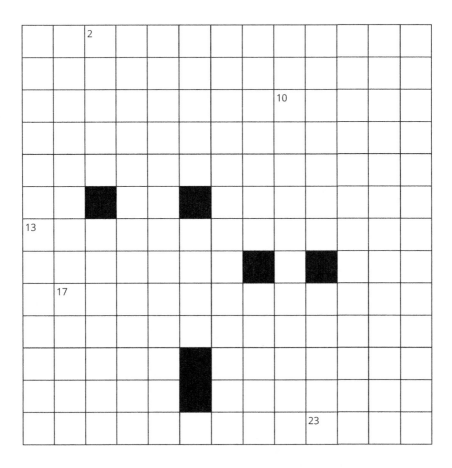

ACROSS: 1 Chances **3** Dolphin-like creature **9** Madagascar and Mauritius, say **10** Rounded shapes **11** Not used to **13** Half diameter **15** Remained **17** Disastrous **20** One-sixteenth of a pound **21** Versus **22** Making less clear **23** Fix

DOWN: 1 Death notice **2** Triangular river mouth **4** Be preoccupied with **5** Scaled in corresponding quantities **6** Foolishly, pointlessly **7** Otherwise **8** Erroneously **12** Taught **14** Removed water from **16** Achieve **18** Door joint **19** Weaving frame

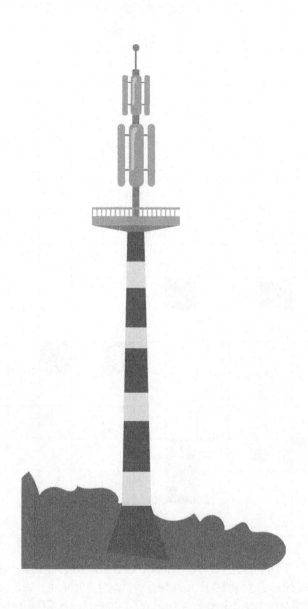

"Did you hear about the antenna towers who got married?
The reception was amazing."

All eight of these single-digit numbers have been removed from this magic square.

Replace the numbers in the grid so that the numbers in the four boxes on each row and in each column total 38.

2   3   4   5   6   7   8   9

	12	15	
14			13
	17	10	
11			16

38

Reading from left to right, from one row onto the next, the five sets of symbols and boxes below follow a sequence. Which of the six boxes from the bottom of the page should come next in the sequence?

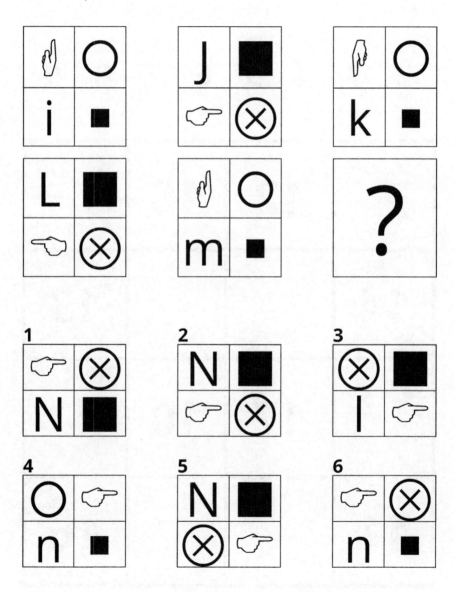

The topic of this crisscross is engineering infrastructure. Put all the words and terms below in the correct places in the grid so that they all connect together.

BROADBAND

CABLE

CONSTRUCTION

DRAINS

ENERGY

FENCES

FLOOD DEFENSES

GRID

INTERNET

LANDSCAPING

POWER

POWER CABLES

ROADS

RAILWAYS

SEWAGE

SYSTEMS

TELECOMMUNICATIONS

TELEVISION

TRANSIT

TRANSPORT

WATER SUPPLY

Each of the squares below contains a number and a directional instruction telling you how many squares to move next, and in which direction.

Starting in the square containing **a multiple of 15**, follow the chain of directions until you reach one of the shaded squares in the center of the grid.

What is the first shaded letter you land in at the end of the chain—A, B, C, or D?

10	67	44	4	17	111	27	64	19
1 RIGHT	4 RIGHT	1 DOWN	2 DOWN	1 RIGHT	1 RIGHT	2 DOWN	3 DOWN	6 LEFT
33	**65**	**9**	**34**	**A**	**70**	**28**	**25**	**40**
1 UP	3 DOWN	2 LEFT	1 DOWN		2 LEFT	1 LEFT	1 LEFT	7 LEFT
91	**36**	**31**	**66**	**B**	**38**	**13**	**34**	**23**
2 DOWN	2 RIGHT	1 LEFT	3 LEFT		1 LEFT	1 DOWN	3 DOWN	1 DOWN
71	**98**	**34**	**67**	**C**	**48**	**95**	**55**	**49**
3 RIGHT	1 DOWN	1 DOWN	5 RIGHT		1 LEFT	1 DOWN	1 LEFT	3 UP
8	**35**	**20**	**6**	**D**	**59**	**48**	**85**	**24**
1 DOWN	1 RIGHT	1 DOWN	1 DOWN		1 DOWN	2 LEFT	1 DOWN	1 DOWN
16	**7**	**33**	**24**	**104**	**7**	**115**	**100**	**45**
3 RIGHT	1 RIGHT	1 RIGHT	2 UP	1 UP	4 UP	1 UP	4 RIGHT	3 LEFT

What direction will Gear B turn if Gear A is turned counterclockwise?

If it ain't broke, don't fix it!
Well, I'm an engineer. So if it ain't broke, add more features.

Complete this grid so that the digits 1–9 appear once and only once in each row, each column, and each smaller 3x3 square of cells.

	6					5	7	3
4	5				7			
7			5			1		
8			4		3	7	2	6
		6	7		2	9		5
3		2		5		8	4	1
5		7			4	3	6	8
6			3		1			9
9	2				5			7

Did you know?

Bronze was the first manmade alloy in history. It was first produced from copper and tin around 4500 BC!

Can you complete this pyramid so that each square contains the sum of the two digits beneath it?

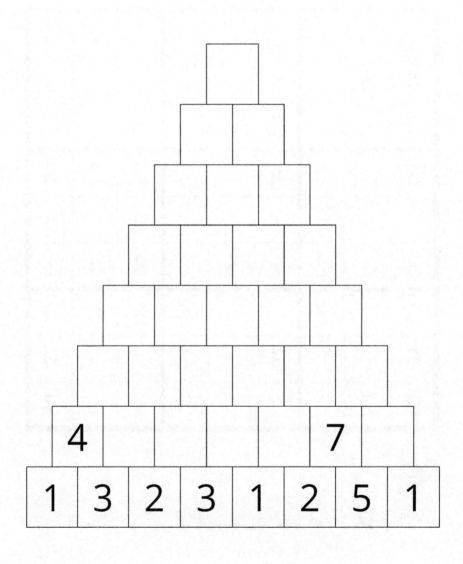

44

Can you find your way through this maze from the opening at the top to the toolkit on the other side?

Take a look at the grid of shapes and symbols below.
In the empty grid beneath it, you must recreate the same
pattern rotated 90° clockwise. Remember, you'll not only need
to rotate the positions of the symbols, but some of the symbols
themselves will not look the same when turned around.

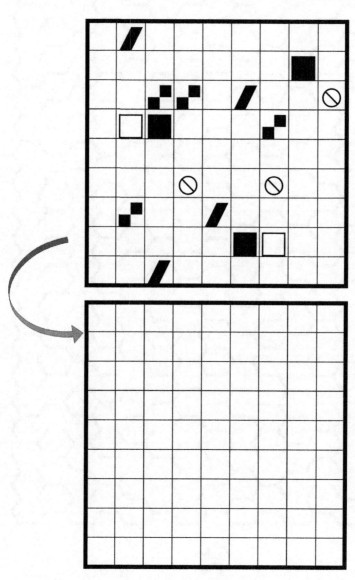

engineer

en·gi·neer [ˌen-jə-ˈnir]

(*n.*) 1. someone who notices things other people don't see

    2. someone who gets excited about things no one else gets excited about

The formula for finding the sum of the internal angles of a shape is (n - 2) x 180, where n is the number of sides. With that in mind, what would be the sum of the internal angles of this shape?

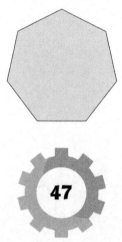

Engineers have a unique skill. They can turn coffee into ... what? To find out the answer, place the correct letter to complete these 5-letter words into the spaces below. Watch out, though—there might be more than one possible solution to each word!

T	A		L	E
S	Q		A	T
C	L		C	K
S	A		E	S
A	D		E	D
W	H		L	E
F	I		E	R
B	E		A	N
B	A		E	S

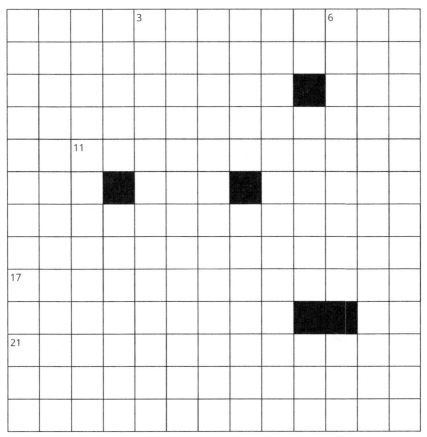

ACROSS: 1 Perturb **5** Powdery remains of a fire **8** Compelled **9** Employ **10** Master of ceremonies **12** Hide **13** Reason **14** Having a flat, even surface **17** Encouraging conversation **19** Enclosed area of water **21** Which person? **22** Instantaneous **24** Word that sounds akin to another **25** Mexican peninsula

DOWN: 1 Love **2** Unwell **3** Fishermen **4** Tempt **5** Extra feature **6** Domestic tasks **7** Sneakiness **11** Discordance **13** Make able to do something **15** Tuneful **16** Of clothing, revealing **18** Living **20** Polished shine **23** Legal decree

49

Use just four straight lines to connect all nine of the circles below.

Did you know?

A number 1 followed by 100 zeroes is known as a *googol!*

50

Time for another sudoku puzzle. Complete this grid so that the digits 1–9 appear once and only once in each row, each column, and each smaller 3x3 square of cells.

4	5		9	2			6	3
2		3	1	4		5		
				6	3	2		
		2			9	7		
9		1					2	
7						3		
			9	1				
	9		3	5	2		7	
	1	5						

Did you know?

The first person to break the sound barrier in an aircraft was Chuck Yeager, way back in 1947!

Why did the software engineer hate the jungle?

There were too many bugs for his liking...

Each of the squares below contains a 3-digit number and a directional instruction telling you how many squares to move next, and in which direction.

Starting in the square containing **a multiple of 17**, follow the chain of directions until you reach one of the shaded squares in the center of the grid.

What is the first shaded letter you land in at the end of the chain—A, B, C, or D?

103 1 DOWN	780 2 DOWN	419 1 RIGHT	412 2 DOWN	511 3 LEFTw	733 3 RIGHT	458 3 DOWN	852 2 DOWN	272 2 LEFT
766 2 RIGHT	444 1 UP	900 1 UP	290 2 DOWN	**A**	970 1 LEFT	562 3 DOWN	443 1 RIGHT	860 1 LEFT
181 2 DOWN	936 2 UP	512 2 LEFT	104 2 DOWN	**B**	273 1 UP	150 2 DOWN	681 2 LEFT	734 1 LEFT
565 3 RIGHT	220 6 RIGHT	373 2 DOWN	460 1 UP	**C**	809 4 LEFT	111 4 LEFT	547 1 UP	550 1 LEFT
777 6 RIGHT	240 1 RIGHT	180 1 RIGHT	490 5 RIGHT	**D**	998 1 DOWN	231 2 UP	937 2 UP	608 1 UP
888 4 UP	113 1 LEFT	590 1 LEFT	559 3 LEFT	154 2 UP	470 2 RIGHT	235 3 LEFT	495 1 UP	810 1 LEFT

Reading from left to right, from one row onto the next, the five sets of symbols and boxes below follow a sequence. Which of the six boxes from the bottom of the page should come next in the sequence?

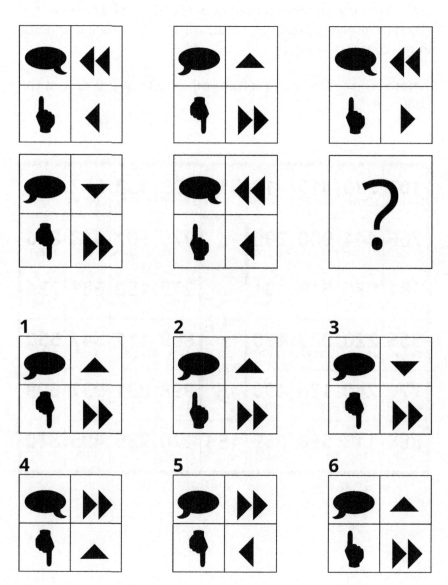

Here's another trio of brain teasers and riddles for you to solve...

A: F precedes G and G precedes H, but H does not precede I, but rather J. N comes before M. And P and Q are as far apart as it is possible for them to be.
What are we talking about?

B: What word meaning let down could you play on a musical instrument?

C: The car turns left, but the tire does not move.
The car turns right, but again this tire does not move.
Suddenly, the car swerves to the left again, and then swerves sharply to the right—but again, this tire does not move.
How is this possible?

Can you complete this pyramid so that each square contains the sum of the two digits beneath it?

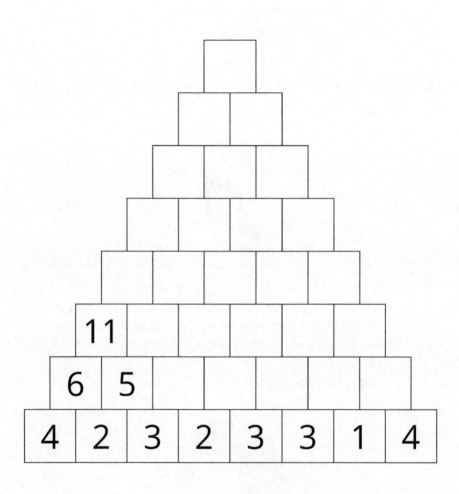

In what direction will Gear B turn if Gear A is rotated counterclockwise?

Take a look at the grid of shapes and symbols below.
In the empty grid beneath it, you must recreate the same pattern
rotated 90° counter-clockwise. Remember, you'll not only need
to rotate the positions of the symbols, but some of the symbols
themselves will not look the same when turned around.

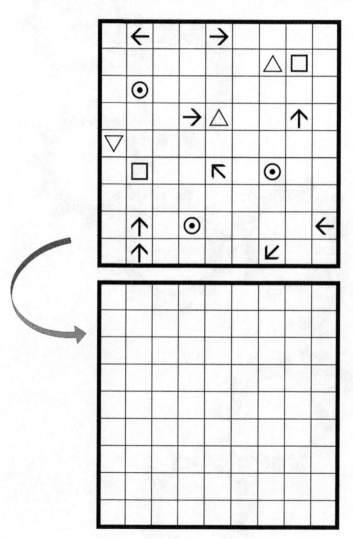

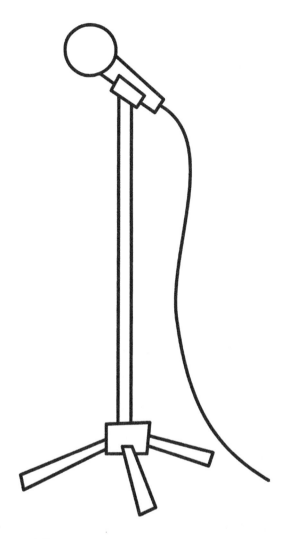

Engineers are great at standup comedy because all their jokes are so well structured!

Math and geometry are the subjects of this crisscross puzzle. Find the correct places for all these words in the connecting grid below.

ALGEBRA

ANGLE

ARC

CALCULUS

CONE

CONIC SECTION

ELLIPSE

EQUATION

EUCLID

GEOMETRY

HYPERBOLA

LIMIT

MATHEMATICS

OPTIMAL

PLANE

POLYGON

PYTHAGOREAN

RIGHT-ANGLE

SURFACE

TANGENT

VERTEX

All nine of the single-digit numbers below 10 have been removed from this magic square. Replace the numbers so that the numbers in the four boxes in each row and each column total 34.

1 2 3 4 5 6 7 8 9

16			13
	11	10	
			12
	14	15	

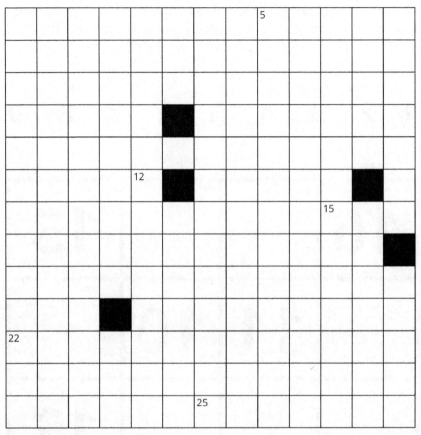

ACROSS: 1 For the reason that **5** Liquid squeezed from fruit **8** Making a supply last **9** Gasping **10** Italian tower **11** One who travels to work **13** Male goose **14** Merely **17** Selects for office **19** Ointment **22** Make less heavy **23** Incompetent **24** Circles **25** Fermented dairy product

DOWN: 1 High-pitched tone **2** Deep shade of red **3** Impel **4** Put to use **5** Unwanted post **6** Dolt **7** Keenly **12** Oversees a negotiation **13** Knotty **15** Area of high flat land **16** Smelly **18** Leaves of a book **20** Musical composition **21** Call

Complete this grid so that the digits 1–9 appear once and only once in each row, each column, and each smaller 3x3 square of cells.

9	7	4						2
	6	1			2	4		
8							6	9
6	4	8	9	5			7	1
							3	
						8	4	
2	8			3	1			4
	3	6	7	2	9			
	9	7		8	5	6	2	3

Did you know?

The world's first remote control was invented in 1901.

Why are structural engineers always so calm?

They have such good stress analysis!

61

Do you know what an engineer's idea of having fun is? They like to solve problems that ... what? To find out the answer, place the correct letter to complete these 5-letter words into the spaces below. Watch out, though—there might be more than one possible solution to each word!

R	I		E	R
M	O		S	E
I	N		E	R
D	E		E	R
N	E		D	S
F	O		E	S
S	P		L	L
M	I		E	R
L	I		E	R
L	A		E	R
S	W		A	T
O	T		E	R

62

The names of three metals are hidden in the words in the following text. What are they?

"With the best intentions, Jacob, alternatively I don't think so. Their only ideas are bad!"

Can you work your way through this maze from the opening at the top to the toolkit on the other side?

Each digit in a standard electronic digital display consists of a combination of up to seven individual lines:

If a standard 24-hour digital clock were ever to read **88:88**, then all 42 possible lines would be illuminated. At **1:11**, however, only six of the lines are illuminated...

...and at **11:11** only eight lines are illuminated across all four digits:

But assuming that the clock reads **0:00** at midnight, then continues **0:01**, **0:02**, **0:03** and so on, what is the earliest time that the clock display will illuminate just eight lines?

Reading from left to right, from one row onto the next, the five sets of symbols and boxes below follow a sequence. Which of the six boxes from the bottom of the page should come next in the sequence?

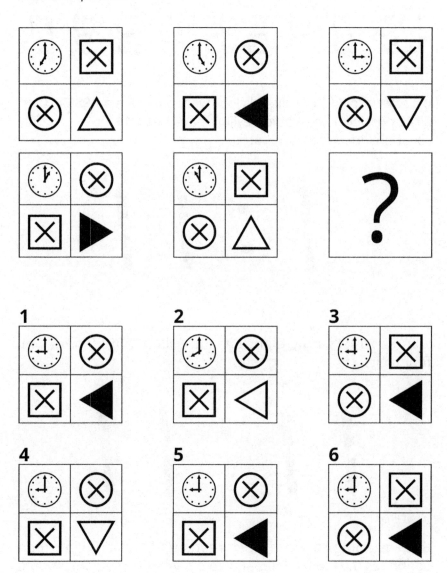

Take a look at the grid of shapes and symbols below.
In the empty grid beneath it, you must recreate the same pattern
rotated 90° counter-clockwise. Remember, you'll not only need
to rotate the positions of the symbols, but some of the symbols
themselves will not look the same when turned around.

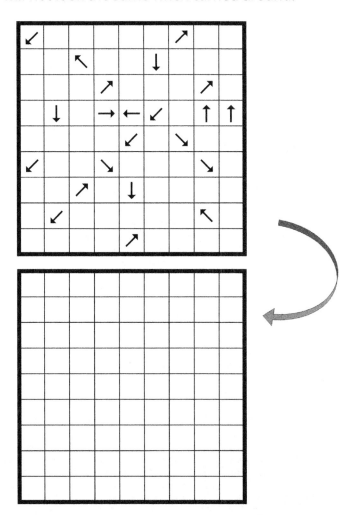

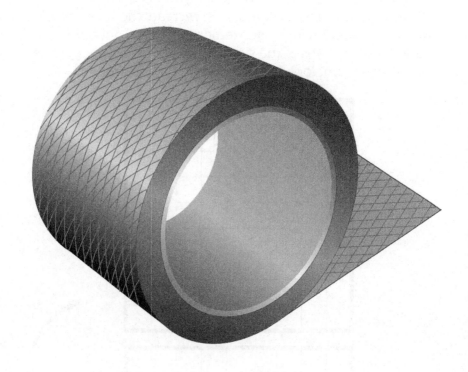

Engineering: where logic and problem-solving meets duct tape

All nine of the single-digit numbers below 10 have been removed from this magic square. Replace the numbers so that the numbers in the four boxes in each row and each column total 37.

1 2 3 4 5 6 7 8 9

	11	17	
16			12
	19		
10			18

68

There's a new housing development being built on the outskirts of town, and the developers have enlisted four experts to cast their eye over the designs: Mr. Henderson, Mr. Hamilton, Mrs. Henley, and Dr. Hoolihan. Each is providing expertise in a different architectural field: one is a structural engineer; another is an expert in strengthened glass; a third works in ventilation; and a fourth is an expert in sustainable design. Each one is due on site a different day this week: Monday, Wednesday, Thursday, and Friday.

Based on the clues on the next page, can you work out who is an expert in what field and when they are due to arrive?

	Structural eng.	Glass	Ventilation	Sustainability	Monday	Wednesday	Thursday	Friday
Mr. Henderson								
Mr. Hamilton								
Mrs. Henley								
Dr. Hoolihan								
Monday								
Wednesday								
Thursday								
Friday								

1. Mr. Hamilton is not arriving on Thursday, and he is not the expert in ventilation.
2. Dr. Hoolihan is arriving on site on Friday. She is not the expert in ventilation, nor in structural engineering.
3. The expert in sustainability is arriving the day after the expert coming to talk about the strengthened glass the developers will need in their design.
4. The expert with a 6-letter surname is arriving on a 6-letter day!

EXPERT	FIELD	DAY
Mr. Henderson		
Mr. Hamilton		
Mrs. Henley		
Dr. Hoolihan		

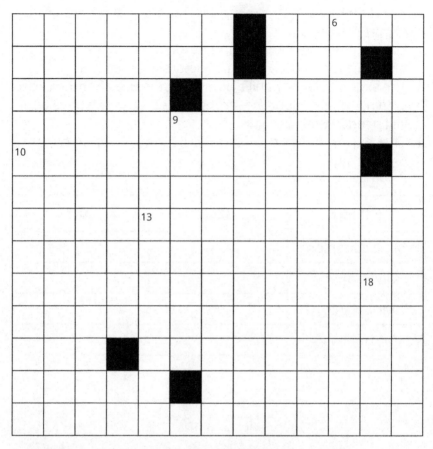

ACROSS: 1 Style of triathlon **5** Wash **8** Illegal activity
9 Having gotten something wrong **10** Wear away
11 Lobby, outer entrance room **14** Put into words
17 Assess **19** Guitar-like instrument **20** Drift on air or water
21 Pass time **22** Periods of tuition

DOWN: 2 Less common **3** Desert wanderers **4** Concept
5 Made and distributed unlawfully **6** Sleeveless style of T-shirt
7 Save **10** Widespread outbreaks **12** Fatuous **13** Askew
15 Matrimonial **16** Constructs **18** Particle

70

This crisscross is dedicated to airspace, aeronautics, and aviation. Find the correct place for all the names and terms below in the grid.

AERODYNAMICS	ENSTROPHY	PROPULSION
AILERON	FLAP	SAIL
AIRSPACE	FLIGHT	SKYHOOK
AICRAFT	FUSELAGE	SONIC BOOM
AVIONICS	LOAD	SPACECRAFT
DRAG	PITCH	TRAJECTORY
EMPENNAGE	PRESSURE	YAW

Complete this grid so that the digits 1–9 appear once and only once in each row, each column, and each smaller 3x3 square of cells.

5			7		6			
			3		5	1	7	2
1	4	7	2			3		6
				5		6		7
6			8		3			9
		5	6		1			3
	7	6		3				5
	5	9			7	2		
4	3			9	2			

Did you know?

Marie Curie was the first person to win two Nobel Prizes.

Mrs. Smith has asked for the lobby of her house to be tiled using perfectly octagonal tiles.

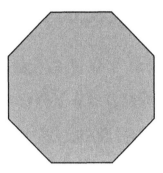

The tiler has come up with a design using a mixture of smaller square and triangular tiles to fill in the gaps between each of the larger octagonal tiles:

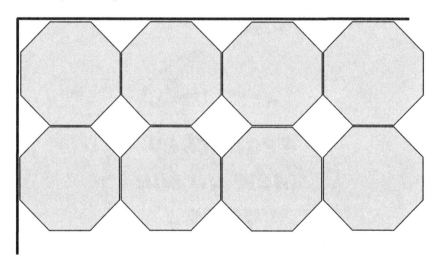

Mrs. Smith's lobby is precisely four octagonal squares wide and five octagonal tiles deep. Including the smaller square and triangle tiles between the octagonal ones, how many tiles will be needed to tile the complete floor?

Did you hear about the engineers of Ancient England?
Yeah, they knew all the angles...

What direction will Gear A turn if Gear B is rotated clockwise?

Can you complete this pyramid so that each square contains the sum of the two digits beneath it?

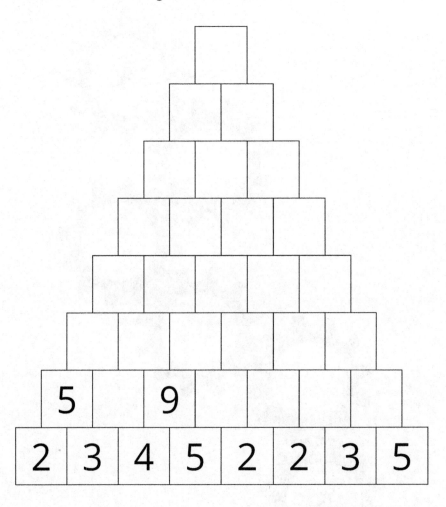

75

What number should come next in this sequence?

0 3 2 5 3 6 3 6 2 5 0 3 -3 0 ?

76

Electrical engineers always make good hires, because they have … what? To find out, place the correct letter to complete these 5-letter words into the spaces below. Watch out, though—there might be more than one possible solution to each word!

D	E		L	T
S	I		L	Y
F	R		N	T
K	I		T	Y
S	P		R	T
O	F		E	R
P	O		P	Y
L	I		N	S
D	O		E	S
N	E		D	Y
M	E		D	S
M	A		E	S
N	A		L	S
S	M		L	L
M	A		L	S

*If at first you don't succeed,
call an engineer.
They won't be able to
help, but they'll be
able to tell you why it
didn't work...*

Take a look at the grid of shapes and symbols below.
In the empty grid beneath it, you must recreate the same
pattern rotated 90° clockwise. Remember, you'll not only need
to rotate the positions of the symbols, but some of the symbols
themselves will not look the same when turned around.

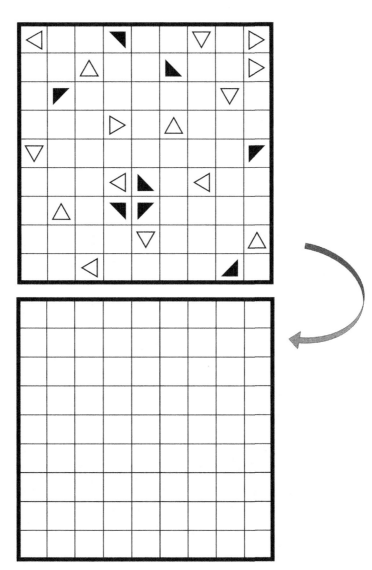

Here are three more fiendish brain teasers to unravel.

A: A man is walking through a snowy field when he stumbles across a body right in the middle of the wide open space. The body is lying face down and appears to be wearing some kind of uniform. He has an unusual kind of backpack attached tightly to his back, with long straps appearing to trail from it. There are no other footsteps leading up to or away from the man, and there is no fresh snow on his back— so the man appears to have appeared from nowhere! Can you solve the case?

B: What are the next two letters in this sequence?

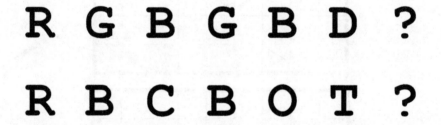

C: Usually in English, male words have to be made longer to make their female equivalent when they share the same root— so ACTRESS is longer than ACTOR. WAITER is shorter than WAITRESS. AVIATOR is shorter than AVIATRIX. And STEWARDESS is definitely longer than STEWARD!
But what 5-letter female word is two letters SHORTER than its male equivalent?

Reading from left to right, from one row onto the next, the five sets of symbols and boxes below follow a sequence. Which of the six boxes from the bottom of the page should come next in the sequence?

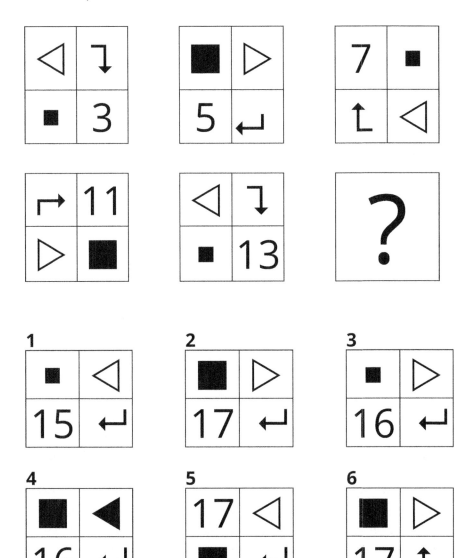

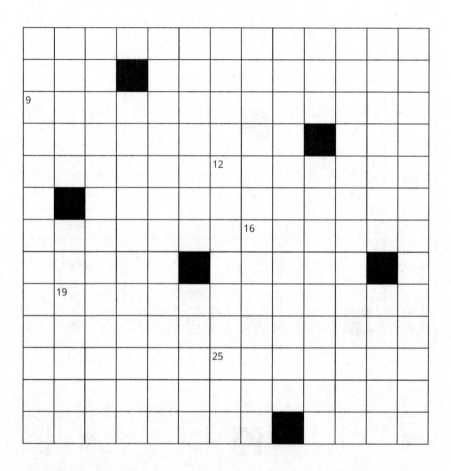

ACROSS: 1 Flying appendage **3** Decorative ribbons **9** Countries
10 Allow **11** Colorless volatile liquid **12** Legal property
14 Crude **16** Thrifty **19** As one **21** Era **24** Fish basket **25** Saying
26 Lack of difficulty **27** Biting fly

DOWN: 1 Imagined **2** Dint **4** Ludicrous **5** Andean mammal
6 Identifying label **7** Takes a seat **8** Quarter **13** Set of letters
15 Tenants **17** Sports brand **18** Alters **20** Bird's claw
22 Sea **23** 4,840 square yards

The single-digit numbers have been removed from this magic square. Replace the ones listed below so that the numbers in the four boxes in each row and in each column total 39.

2   3   4   5   6   7   8   9

	12	16	
15			13
	18	10	
11			17

Why did the engineer bring a ladder to the bar?

He heard the drinks were on the house...

Complete this grid so that the digits 1–9 appear once and only once in each row, each column, and each smaller 3x3 square of cells.

6	8	9		5		1		2
		7		2			3	6
5	2			6			9	8
3	7			4	1	8	2	
8	9	2		3				
				8			5	3
9	5				6	3		
	3	1	4		8			5
2	6	8		7			4	

Did you know?

The first transatlantic television signal was broadcast in 1962.

How many squares are there in total in the figure below?

Each of the squares below contains the symbol of a chemical element and a directional instruction telling you how many squares to move next, and in which direction.

Starting in the square containing **the symbol of element with the atomic number 7**—a gas at room temperature, which is the main constituent of air—follow the chain of directions until you reach one of the shaded squares in the center of the grid.

What is the first shaded letter you land in at the end of the chain—A, B, C, or D?

K	Li	Sr	Al	Sm	Ra	I	Ni	Ac
3 RIGHT	3 RIGHT	2 DOWN	3 DOWN	3 RIGHT	2 DOWN	3 DOWN	1 RIGHT	6 DOWN
Re	**Si**	**W**	**H**	**A**	**Pt**	**Se**	**Mg**	**Co**
7 RIGHT	1 UP	2 RIGHT	1 UP		1 RIGHT	3 DOWN	2 DOWN	2 DOWN
Sc	**O**	**Na**	**Ca**	**B**	**F**	**Cu**	**Ga**	**Ge**
2 RIGHT	1 UP	2 DOWN	1 RIGHT		1 LEFT	2 LEFT	6 LEFT	6 LEFT
Be	**Hf**	**He**	**Po**	**C**	**Db**	**N**	**As**	**Sg**
4 RIGHT	3 RIGHT	2 DOWN	1 RIGHT		3 LEFT	4 LEFT	1 DOWN	1 LEFT
Hg	**Mo**	**Pd**	**Mo**	**D**	**P**	**Ba**	**Eu**	**Lr**
3 UP	3 RIGHT	1 RIGHT	3 LEFT		1 DOWN	1 LEFT	2 DOWN	1 LEFT
Fr	**K**	**Xe**	**Zn**	**E**	**V**	**Sb**	**Nb**	**Rf**
3 UP	1 LEFT	5 RIGHT	1 RIGHT		2 LEFT	3 UP	3 UP	1 DOWN
B	**Mt**	**Ar**	**Bi**	**In**	**Tc**	**Sn**	**Cs**	**Pb**
2 RIGHT	1 UP	2 RIGHT	2 LEFT	4 LEFT	5 UP	3 UP	2 LEFT	7 LEFT

85

We're heading underground for this crisscross puzzle, dedicated to everything and anything to do with subterranean engineering works. Find the correct places for all these terms in the grid below.

ADIT

BACKFILL

BEDROCK

BYPRODUCT

BLASTHOLE

DRAWPOINT

DYKE

EARTHWORKS

EMBANKMENT

EMISSION

FALSEWORK

GRADE

GUIDE

K-RAIL

METRO SYSTEM

ORE

OUTCROP

ROD

SENSOR

SHORING

SUBWAY

SURVEY

TRENCH

VEIN

YIELD

Take a look at the grid of shapes and symbols below.
In the empty grid beneath it, you must recreate the same pattern
rotated 270° counter-clockwise. Remember, you'll not only need
to rotate the positions of the symbols, but some of the symbols
themselves will not look the same when turned around.

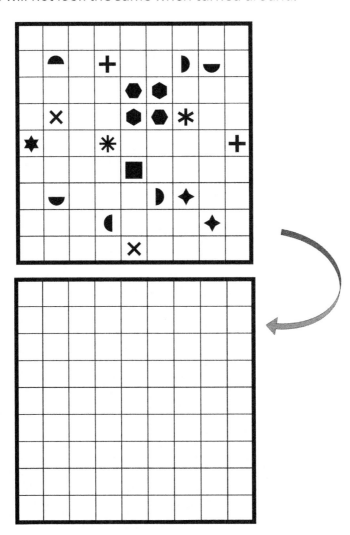

87

Three units of linear measurement are hidden in this sentence. What are they?

"He's working as an engineer in China. Really arduous work, but he's met really interesting people."

88

Engineers. Solving tomorrow's problems with ... what? To find out the answer, place the correct letter to complete these 5-letter words into the spaces below. Watch out, though—there might be more than one possible solution to each word!

W	A		E	R
S	T		O	L
U	N		E	R
T	O		D	S
B	U		E	R
L	I		T	S
P	I		K	S
S	P		T	S
O	F		E	R
W	A		E	R
R	E		D	S
A	V		R	T

How do you flirt with an engineer?

Talk nerdy to them.

89

Five new members of staff—Mr. Watkins, Ms. Wilkins, Dr. Walton, Dr. Wells, and Professor Williams—are joining the engineering department at the local college this semester.

They are each an expert in a different field: one is a mechanical engineer; another is a renowned robotics engineer; someone else is at the forefront of biomedicine and will be teaching biomedical engineering; another is a highly regarded expert in marine engineering; and the fifth is an expert software engineer.

Each one will be based in a different room, too, across the engineering department's four lettered stories: one will be in Room A2, another in Room B4, another two in the side-by-side Rooms C3 and C4; and the last on the top floor, in Room D10.

Based on the clues on the next page, can you work out who will be teaching what this semester and in what room will they be based?

1. The new robotics teacher has an L in their surname.
2. The two members of staff who will be neighbors in C block at the college also have the same number of letters in their surnames.
3. The expert in biomedical engineering will be teaching in room A2. They are neither of the doctors.
4. The person in room C3 is not a software engineer, and the person in room B4 is neither the expert in mechanics nor robotics.
5. The staff member with the shortest name—who is not the robotics expert—will be teaching in the room with the highest number.

	Mechanics	Robotics	Biomedicine	Marine science	Software	A2	B4	C3	C4	D10
Mr. Watkins										
Ms. Wilkins										
Dr. Walton										
Dr. Wells										
Prof. Williams										
A2					
B4					
C3					
C4					
D10					

TEACHER	SUBJECT	ROOM
Mr. Watkins		
Ms. Wilkins		
Dr. Walton		
Dr. Wells		
Prof. Williams		

What direction will Gears B and C turn if Gear A rotates counterclockwise?

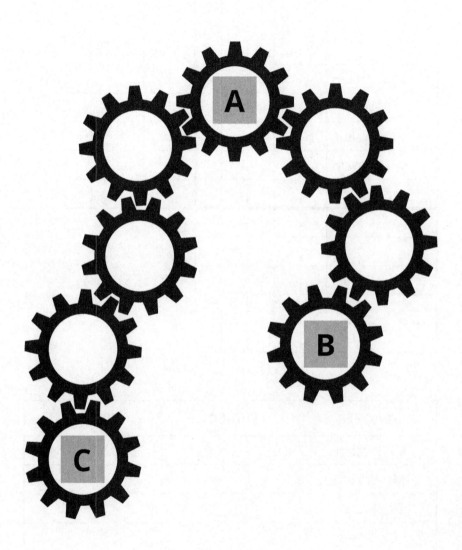

Can you complete this pyramid so that each square contains the sum of the two digits beneath it?

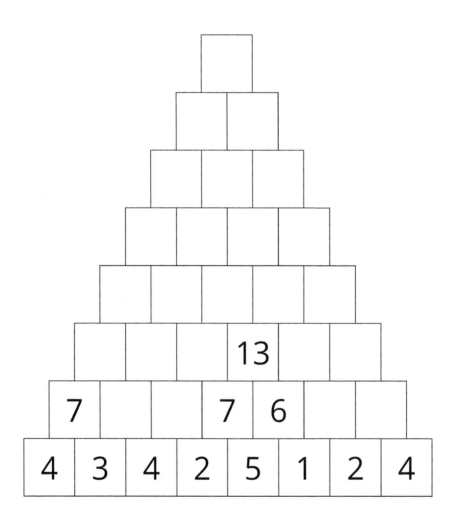

Complete this grid so that the digits 1–9 appear once and only once in each row, each column, and each smaller 3x3 square of cells.

	6	3	5	7		1		2
5			9	4			7	
	7	8	6			4		5
		7		1		3		4
			3	8	6			
					7			9
			1		5	2		
	2		8				1	3
1	4	5					6	

Did you know?

The most frequently struck key on a qwerty keyboard isn't a letter—it's the space bar!

93

Reading from left to right, from one row onto the next, the five sets of symbols and boxes below follow a sequence. Which of the six boxes from the bottom of the page should come next in the sequence?

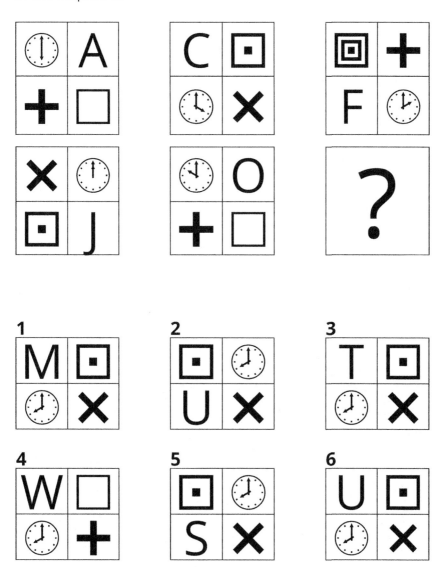

How do you catch a software engineer?

With a mouse trap!

Can you work your way through this maze from the opening at the top to the toolkit on the other side?

Take a look at the grid of shapes and symbols below.
In the empty grid beneath it, you must recreate the same pattern rotated 90° counter-clockwise. Remember, you'll not only need to rotate the positions of the symbols, but some of the symbols themselves will not look the same when turned around.

Did you hear about that expert in torque friction? He really progressed in his career, because he was so good at … what? To find out the answer, place the correct letter to complete these 5-letter words into the spaces below. Watch out, though—there might be more than one possible solution to each word!

A	C		O	R
R	O		E	R
M	O		S	T
L	O		E	S
P	I		C	H
O	N		O	N
T	E		O	N
A	R		O	N
R	E		D	Y
M	E		I	T
L	I		I	T
P	O		E	S

What number should come next in this sequence?

3 6 5 10 8 16 13 26 22 44 ?

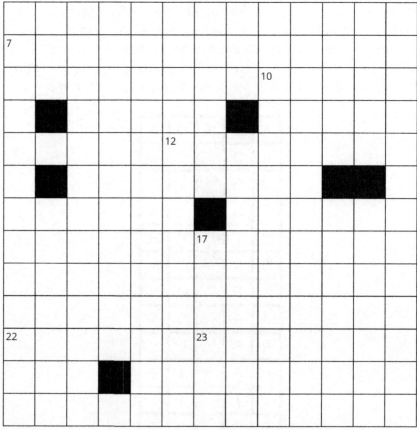

ACROSS: 1 Not matching or like the rest **9** Dawdles
10 Unsuccessful person **11** Long-billed waterbird **12** Double-cross **14** Raids **15** International **18** Promise again **20** Fluid-filled growth **22** Explode **23** Keepsake **24** Dramatists

DOWN: 2 Louder **3** Not closed **4** Talkative person **5** Improbable **6** Make sad **7** Misguided **8** Hardship, adverse circumstances **13** Uniformity across an axis **16** Blade attached to a rifle **17** Cook on a low boil **19** Heartless **21** Air pollution

Here's a final trio of brain teasers for you to solve...

A: Rearrange each of these words to spell another.
What do those three new words all have in common?

FLESHER

STIFLE

FLEMISH

B: What comes next in this sequence?

3T 4S 5P 6H
7H 8O 9D ?

C: The name of what everyday item of office equipment is a 9-letter word that begins with P, ends with P, and has a third letter P somewhere in between?

100

Why was the electrical engineer in such good shape? Because he was always running circuits, of course! Electronics is the subject of this final mega crisscross challenge, which has no less than 50 words to find homes for. To help you out, we've arranged them by length for you, as well as alphabetically.

3 letters
AMP
LCD
MHO
OHM
SNR

4 letters
BYTE
FLOW
GATE
GOBO
IGBT
LINE
NEON
PAIR
RAIL

5 letters
HERTZ
INPUT
MODEM
MOUSE
RADAR
SURGE

6 letters
CAMERA
FILTER
LINKER
NONODE
PLASMA
REMOTE
SLEEVE
TRIODE

7 letters
AIRWAVE
FOURIER

8 letters
ELECTRON
FLIPFLOP
REALTIME
RESISTOR
ROBOTICS

9 letters
MODULATOR
POTENTIAL
VOLTMETER

10 letters
PARAFORMER
PEAK TO PEAK
REED SWITCH

11 letters
STEADY-STATE

12 letters
AUTO-RECLOSER
KILOWATT-HOUR

14 letters
NOISE REDUCTION
RADIO FREQUENCY

15 letters
MECHANICAL FAULT

16 letters
SUBMARINE CABLING

17 letters
QUADRATURE BOOSTER

19 letters
PULSECODEMODULATION

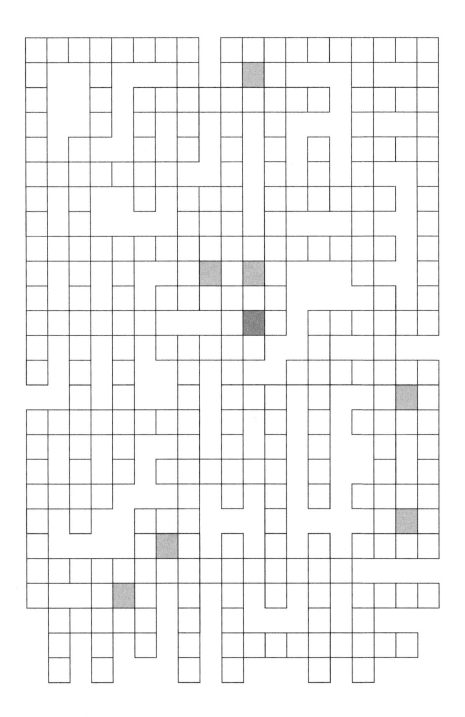

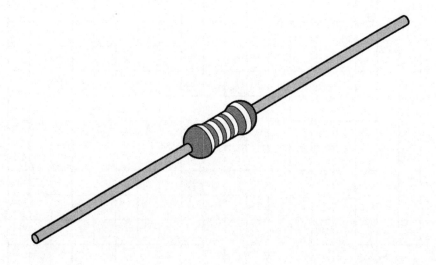

**Engineers can never
resistor final pun...**

CONCLUSION

Congratulations!

With that final mega-challenging crisscross puzzle, your book of *Brain Teasers for Smart Engineers* is complete!

So how did you do? Are you officially a Smart Engineer?

Did you find these puzzles simple, tricky, or downright impossible? Did you find yourself flying through them, as if there were no challenge here at all?

Or did you find yourself putting the book down to come back to later, or even—perish the thought!—dipping into the solutions for a quick hint or a nudge in the right direction?

Well, no matter how you've fared here, hopefully the last 120 pages or so of puzzles, games, riddles, number challenges (and a few japes and one-liners!) have not only kept you entertained but given your brain a little workout too. And along the way, hopefully we've done a little something to celebrate the wonderful world of engineering—from electronics and robotics, to mathematics, geometry, mechanics, construction, aeronautics, and everything else besides.

But for now, you've earned a break—and can kick back and put your feet up knowing full well that you're a Smart Engineer!

SOLUTIONS

1

	A	S	K	I	N	G	P	R	I	C	E	
I		I		A		E		E		U		N
M	O	D	E	M		N	A	M	I	B	I	A
P		E		B		I		A		E		U
E	T	C	H		G	U	A	R	D	D	O	G
R		A		K		S		K				H
F	A	R	C	E	S		T	E	A	S	E	T
E				E		E		D		I		I
C	A	C	K	L	I	N	G		C	L	A	N
T		E		H		Z		S		I		E
L	U	L	L	A	B	Y		P	I	C	K	S
Y		L		U		M		U		O		S
	F	O	O	L	S	E	R	R	A	N	D	

3

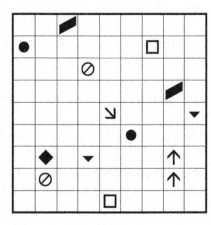

2

4	2	3	1	9	5	8	7	6
8	1	7	2	3	6	9	5	4
5	9	6	8	7	4	3	1	2
2	6	8	4	5	7	1	3	9
7	3	9	6	2	1	4	8	5
1	5	4	9	8	3	2	6	7
3	4	5	7	1	2	6	9	8
9	7	2	3	6	8	5	4	1
6	8	1	5	4	9	7	2	3

4

Starting in square 51, you end up in square A.

5

110 steps.
The next palindromic number is 8,118.

6

The number 8. When rotated through 90°, it becomes the infinity sign ∞ !

7

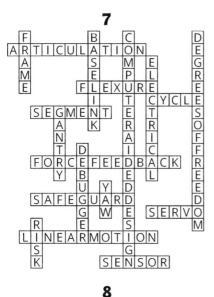

10

MECHANIC	VEHICLE	DAY
Bob	Motorcycle	Wednesday
Craig	Sports car	Monday
Gary	School bus	Tuesday
Phil	Monster truck	Friday

11

7	3	6	8	2	1	4	9	5
9	4	1	6	3	5	7	2	8
5	2	8	7	9	4	1	6	3
1	9	2	4	5	7	8	3	6
8	6	4	2	1	3	5	7	9
3	7	5	9	6	8	2	1	4
6	5	9	1	8	2	3	4	7
4	1	3	5	7	9	6	8	2
2	8	7	3	4	6	9	5	1

8

There are 13 squares.

9

Number 6

The top left square is switching from black to white; the semicircle in the top right is rotating 90° each time; and the bottom two symbols are switching places.

12

13

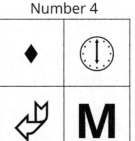

P	U	C	K		D	E	S	C	R	I	B	E
R		I		C		R		O		N		A
O	U	T	D	O	O	R		N	E	S	T	S
V		E		M				V		E		Y
I	N	D	E	P	E	N	D	E	N	C	E	
N			O		Y		N		T		R	
C	A	P		S	P	L	I	T		S	H	E
E		R		I		O		I				C
	C	O	N	T	I	N	U	O	U	S	L	Y
S		P		I			N		I		C	
P	R	O	M	O		C	H	A	N	N	E	L
O		S		N		A		L		C		E
T	R	E	A	S	U	R	E		N	E	E	D

14

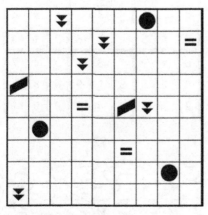

15

Flask B, because water at 25°F would be frozen solid!

16

2. Opposite numbers on a die should always total 7, so with 2 opposite 5 it would appear where 4 is now.

17

Number 4

The diamond is the top left is getting smaller in three stages, so must be the smallest in the sixth box. The clock is advancing one hour each time, but it is switching places with the letter beside it, which is advancing through the alphabet by two letters. The folded arrow in the bottom left is rotating clockwise and so must be folded downwards and pointing to the left again in the sixth box.

18

Beginning in square 54, you end in square B.

19

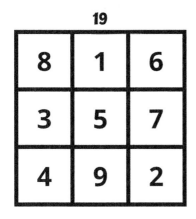

8	1	6
3	5	7
4	9	2

22

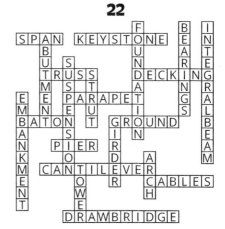

```
S P A N   K E Y S T O N E            F        B E            I N
      B            S                  O        E              N T
      U   T R U S S           D E C K I N G    A              E
      T   S       T           U                R              G R
      M   S       R   P A R A P E T             I              R A
E     E   E       U           A                N              A L
M     N   N       T   G R O U N D               G              L B
B A T O N S       T           I                 S              E A
A     S           I R D                                         A M
N         P I E R   O   D               A                       M
K         O         W   D               R
M         C A N T I L E V E R           C A B L E S
E         O         W                   H
N         W E
T         D R A W B R I D G E
```

20

The code is 453.

21

2	6	4	9	3	8	5	7	1
5	9	3	2	1	7	8	4	6
7	8	1	6	5	4	2	3	9
1	7	8	5	4	6	3	9	2
4	3	2	1	7	9	6	8	5
6	5	9	8	2	3	7	1	4
8	1	7	4	6	2	9	5	3
3	2	5	7	9	1	4	6	8
9	4	6	3	8	5	1	2	7

23

24

C	H	I	D	E		B	U	C	K	E	T	S
	O		E		S		N		I		O	
C	O	N	F	E	C	T	I	O	N	E	R	Y
	P		O		E		T		D		M	
		C	R	A	N	B	E	R	R	I	E	S
	E		E		T		D		E		N	
A	N	G	S	T				E	D	I	T	S
	C		T		A		B		S		S	
M	I	S	A	N	T	H	R	O	P	E		
	R		T		H		O		I		U	
A	C	C	I	D	E	N	T	P	R	O	N	E
	L		O		N		H		I		D	
K	E	E	N	E	S	T		E	T	H	O	S

25

It would have 12 square faces.

26

Clockwise

27

There are 12 squares in total.

28

Number 3

The numbers in the top left square are advancing in a Fibonacci sequence and are the sum of the previous two numbers. The top right chevron is rotating counterclockwise 90° each time, while the arrow on the bottom row is rotating 45° each time and swapping places with the ticks and crosses in the box beside it. The ticks and crosses are switching in and out of checkboxes; a tick in a checkbox would be next.

29

Beginning in square 48, you end in square C.

30

"Take the best that exists and make it better. When it does not exist, design it."
(Sir Henry Royce)

31

30° (one-twelfth of a full circle).

32

1	4	7	5	3	2	8	9	6
3	5	6	9	8	1	7	2	4
8	2	9	6	7	4	5	3	1
7	6	3	1	4	9	2	8	5
9	8	5	2	6	7	1	4	3
2	1	4	8	5	3	9	6	7
5	9	1	4	2	6	3	7	8
6	7	8	3	9	5	4	1	2
4	3	2	7	1	8	6	5	9

33

CLASSMATE	SUBJECT	PLACEMENT
Graham	Transport	Local council
Hannah	Architecture	Abroad
Isaiah	Electrics	Family business
John	Manufacturing	Agency

34

35

A: A sundial has the fewest moving parts, with none. An hourglass or sand timer has the most, with many thousands of individual grains of sand.

B: S. Beginning in springtime, the letters are the initials of the consecutive months of the year—March, April, May, June, July, and August. Next would come S for September.

C: The three pairs are 113 and 131, 137 and 173, and 179 and 197.

36

O	D	D	S		P	O	R	P	O	I	S	E
B		E		I		B		R		N		L
I	S	L	A	N	D	S		O	V	A	L	S
T		T		A		E		P		N		E
U	N	A	C	C	U	S	T	O	M	E	D	
A				C		S		R		L		E
R	A	D	I	U	S		S	T	A	Y	E	D
Y		R		R		A		I				U
	C	A	T	A	S	T	R	O	P	H	I	C
L		I		T		T		N		I		A
O	U	N	C	E		A	G	A	I	N	S	T
O		E		L		I		L		G		E
M	U	D	D	Y	I	N	G		M	E	N	D

37

9	12	15	2
14	3	8	13
4	17	10	7
11	6	5	16

39

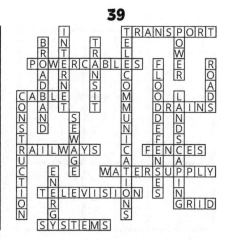

38

Number 2

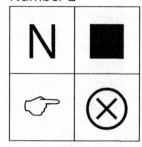

The top and bottom rows are switching places each time. The letter is progressing through the alphabet, alternating upper and lower case. The circle has a cross mark in it in every second box. The pointing hand is rotating 90° each time. The square is switching back and forth from large to small.

40

Starting in square 45, you end in square D.

41

Counterclockwise.

42

2	6	1	9	4	8	5	7	3
4	5	8	1	3	7	6	9	2
7	3	9	5	2	6	1	8	4
8	9	5	4	1	3	7	2	6
1	4	6	7	8	2	9	3	5
3	7	2	6	5	9	8	4	1
5	1	7	2	9	4	3	6	8
6	8	4	3	7	1	2	5	9
9	2	3	8	6	5	4	1	7

43

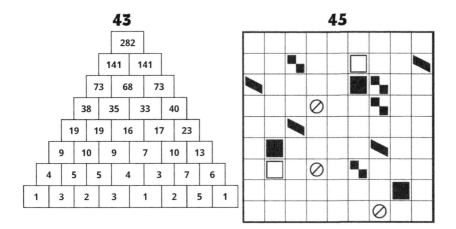

			282				
		141	141				
	73	68	73				
38	35	33	40				
19	19	16	17	23			
9	10	9	7	10	13		
4	5	5	4	3	7	6	
1	3	2	3	1	2	5	1

44

45

46

900°. The figure is a heptagon, with seven sides, so the sum of the angles would be (7 - 2) x 180, which is 900.

47

T	A	B	L	E
S	Q	U	A	T
C	L	I	C	K
S	A	L	E	S
A	D	D	E	D
W	H	I	L	E
F	I	N	E	R
B	E	G	A	N
B	A	S	E	S

ANSWER: Buildings!

48

A	G	I	T	A	T	E		A	S	H	E	S
D	L		N		N	D	O		O			T
O	B	L	I	G	A	T	E	D		U	S	E
R			L		I		O			S		A
E	M	C	E	E		C	O	N	C	E	A	L
	A		R		E			W				T
E	X	C	U	S	E		S	M	O	O	T	H
M		O			S		E					R
P	E	P	T	A	L	K		L	A	K	E	S
O		H		L		I		O				H
W	H	O		I	M	M	E	D	I	A	T	E
E		N		V		P		I		C		E
R	H	Y	M	E		Y	U	C	A	T	A	N

51

Beginning in square 272, you will end up in Square A.

52

Number 1

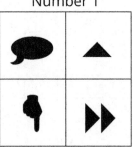

The tail on the speech bubble in the top left is switching from left to right each time. The pointing finger is alternating between pointing upwards and downwards. The two squares containing triangles are switching back and forth, one above the other. In the square containing the single tringle, the triangle is rotating 90° each time; in the square containing the paired triangles, the triangles are swapping direction each time.

49

One solution is as follows:

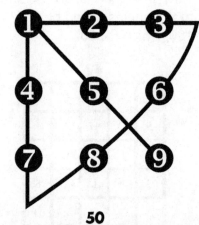

50

4	5	8	9	2	7	1	6	3
2	6	3	1	4	8	5	9	7
1	7	9	5	6	3	2	8	4
5	4	6	2	3	9	7	1	8
9	3	1	7	8	5	4	2	6
7	8	2	4	1	6	3	5	9
3	2	7	6	9	1	8	4	5
8	9	4	3	5	2	6	7	1
6	1	5	8	7	4	9	3	2

53

A: The layout of a qwerty keyboard

B: The word DEFLATED—which can be played as D, E flat, and D.

C: It's the spare tire.

56

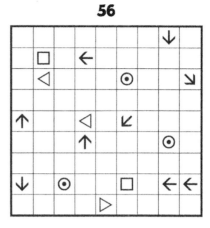

54

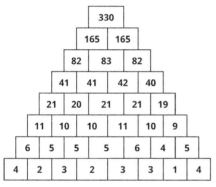

55

Clockwise.

57

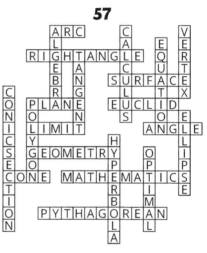

58

16	2	3	13
5	11	10	8
9	7	6	12
4	14	15	1

59

B	E	C	A	U	S	E		J	U	I	C	E
L		R		R	M		U		D		A
E	K	I	N	G		P	A	N	T	I	N	G
E		M		E		L		K		O		E
P	I	S	A		C	O	M	M	U	T	E	R
		O		M		Y		A				L
G	A	N	D	E	R		S	I	M	P	L	Y
N				D		S		L		L	
A	P	P	O	I	N	T	S		B	A	L	M
R		A		A		I		R		T		O
L	I	G	H	T	E	N		I	N	E	P	T
E		E		E		K		N		A		E
D	I	S	C	S		Y	O	G	H	U	R	T

60

9	7	4	5	6	8	3	1	2
5	6	1	3	9	2	4	8	7
8	2	3	1	7	4	5	6	9
6	4	8	9	5	3	2	7	1
7	1	2	8	4	6	9	3	5
3	5	9	2	1	7	8	4	6
2	8	5	6	3	1	7	9	4
4	3	6	7	2	9	1	5	8
1	9	7	4	8	5	6	2	3

61

R	I	D	E	R
M	O	O	S	E
I	N	N	E	R
D	E	T	E	R
N	E	E	D	S
F	O	X	E	S
S	P	I	L	L
M	I	S	E	R
L	I	T	E	R
L	A	Y	E	R
S	W	E	A	T
O	T	T	E	R

ANSWER: Don't exist yet!

62

Tin, cobalt, and iron:
"With the besT INtentions, JaCOB, ALTernatively I don't think so. TheIR ONly ideas are bad!"

63

64
1.14 in the morning

65
Number 5

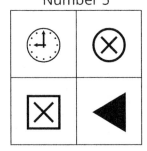

The clock in the top left is reversing by two hours each time. The two crosses, circular and square, are switching places diagonally with each pass. The triangle in the bottom right box is rotating 90° each time and switching between black and white.

66

		←			
	↖	←		↗	✔
↖			↗		
	→	↘			
		↓	↘	→	↖
	↖	↑		↗	
	✔			↖	
		→			↘
↘				↘	

67

8	11	17	1
16	2	7	12
3	19	9	6
10	5	4	18

68

EXPERT	FIELD	DAY
Mr. Henderson	Glass	Thursday
Mr. Hamilton	Structural engineering	Wednesday
Mrs. Henley	Ventilation	Monday
Dr. Hoolihan	Sustainability	Friday

71

5	2	3	7	1	6	8	9	4
9	6	8	3	4	5	1	7	2
1	4	7	2	8	9	3	5	6
3	8	2	9	5	4	6	1	7
6	1	4	8	7	3	5	2	9
7	9	5	6	2	1	4	8	3
2	7	6	1	3	8	9	4	5
8	5	9	4	6	7	2	3	1
4	3	1	5	9	2	7	6	8

69

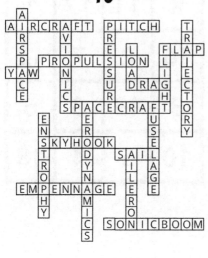

70

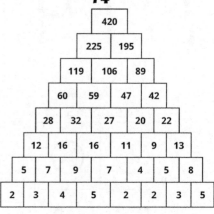

72

The design will require 50 tiles.

73

Counterclockwise.

74

```
                  420
              225     195
           119    106    89
        60    59    47    42
     28   32    27    20   22
   12   16   16   11    9   13
  5    7    9    7    4    5    8
2    3    4    5    2    2    3    5
```

75

-7. The sequence is plus 3, minus 1; plus 3, minus 2; plus 3, minus 3; and so on.

76

D	E	A	L	T
S	I	L	L	Y
F	R	O	N	T
K	I	T	T	Y
S	P	O	R	T
O	F	F	E	R
P	O	P	P	Y
L	I	O	N	S
D	O	T	E	S
N	E	E	D	Y
M	E	N	D	S
M	A	T	E	S
N	A	I	L	S
S	M	A	L	L
M	A	L	L	S

ANSWER: A lot of potential!

77

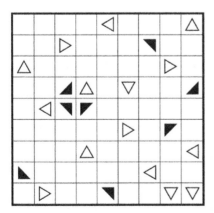

78

A: The man was a parachutist whose parachute failed to open.

B: J and B. Split across the two rows are the consecutive names of US Presidents: Ronald Reagan, George Bush, Bill Clinton, George (W) Bush, Barack Obama, and Donald Trump. Next would be Joe Biden, so there needs to be a J on the top row, and a B on the bottom.

C: WIDOW is two letters shorter than WIDOWER.

79
Number 2

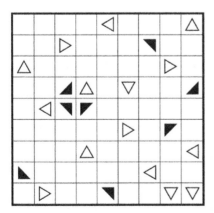

All four boxes are rotating clockwise with each step. The 90° arrow is showing the rotation each time; behind it, the white triangle is changing direction from left to right with each pass; behind that, the black square is alternating between small and large; and the numbers are following a prime number sequence, so next after 13 must be 17.

80

W	I	N	G		G	A	R	L	A	N	D	S
O	O	F		B		L		A				I
N	A	T	I	O	N	S		A	D	M	I	T
D		C		U		U		M		E		S
E	T	H	E	R		R	E	A	L	T	Y	
R			T		D				A			A
E	A	R	T	H	Y		F	R	U	G	A	L
D		E			A		E					P
	U	N	I	T	E	D		E	P	O	C	H
A		T		A		A		B		C		A
C	R	E	E	L		P	R	O	V	E	R	B
R		R		O		T		K		A		E
E	A	S	I	N	E	S	S		G	N	A	T

82

6	8	9	3	5	4	1	7	2
4	1	7	8	2	9	5	3	6
5	2	3	1	6	7	4	9	8
3	7	5	6	4	1	8	2	9
8	9	2	7	3	5	6	1	4
1	4	6	9	8	2	7	5	3
9	5	4	2	1	6	3	8	7
7	3	1	4	9	8	2	6	5
2	6	8	5	7	3	9	4	1

83

There are 40 squares in total.

81

9	12	16	2
15	3	8	13
4	18	10	7
11	6	5	17

84

Beginning in square N (for nitrogen), you will end up in Square E.

85

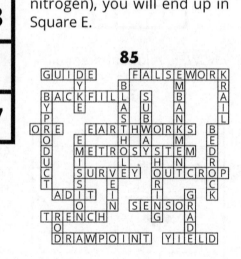

86

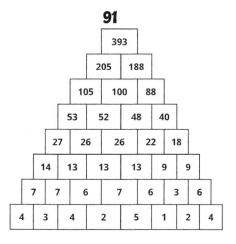

89

TEACHER	SUBJECT	ROOM
Mr. Watkins	Software	C4
Ms. Wilkins	Robotics	C3
Dr. Walton	Marine science	B4
Dr. Wells	Mechanics	D10
Prof. Williams	Biomedicine	A2

90

Gear B will turn clockwise, and Gear C will turn counterclockwise.

87

Inch, yard, and metre:
"He's working as an engineer IN CHina. ReallY ARDuous work, but he's MET REally interesting people."

91

			393			
		205	188			
	105	100	88			
	53	52	48	40		
27	26	26	22	18		
14	13	13	13	9	9	
7	7	6	7	6	3	6
4	3	4	2	5	1	2	4

88

W	A	T	E	R
S	T	O	O	L
U	N	D	E	R
T	O	A	D	S
B	U	Y	E	R
L	I	S	T	S
P	I	C	K	S
S	P	O	T	S
O	F	F	E	R
W	A	F	E	R
R	E	E	D	S
A	V	E	R	T

ANSWER: Today's coffee!

92

4	6	3	5	7	8	1	9	2
5	1	2	9	4	3	8	7	6
9	7	8	6	2	1	4	3	5
6	5	7	2	1	9	3	8	4
2	9	4	3	8	6	7	5	1
3	8	1	4	5	7	6	2	9
8	3	9	1	6	5	2	4	7
7	2	6	8	9	4	5	1	3
1	4	5	7	3	2	9	6	8

Number 6

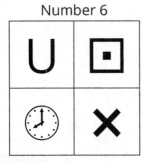

All four symbols are rotating counterclockwise. The clock is moving backwards two hours with each move. The cross is rotating 45° with each move. The square is gaining a smaller square inside, then a second square around that, then losing that second square, then losing the smaller square, cyclically. The letters are progressing through the alphabet, but missing one letter out, then two letters, then three, and so on in the sequence A (B), C (DE), F (GHI), J (KLMN), O (PQRST), U.

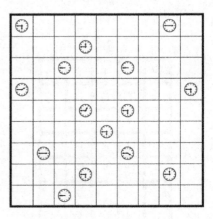

A	C	T	O	R
R	O	W	E	R
M	O	I	S	T
L	O	S	E	S
P	I	T	C	H
O	N	I	O	N
T	E	N	O	N
A	R	G	O	N
R	E	A	D	Y
M	E	R	I	T
L	I	M	I	T
P	O	S	E	S

ANSWER: Twisting arms!

97

39. The sequence doubles the first digit, then takes away 1 from the result; then doubles the next digit, and subtracts 2 from the result; then doubles that, and subtracts 3 from the result, and so on. 44 minus 5 is ultimately 39.

98

	I	N	C	O	N	G	R	U	O	U	S	
I		O	P		A		N		P		T	
L	O	I	T	E	R	S		L	O	S	E	R
L		S		N		B		I		E		I
I	B	I	S		B	A	C	K	S	T	A	B
N		E		S		G		E				U
F	O	R	A	Y	S		G	L	O	B	A	L
O				M		S		Y		A		A
R	E	C	O	M	M	I	T		C	Y	S	T
M		R		E		M		S		O		I
E	R	U	P	T		M	E	M	E	N	T	O
D		E		R		E		O		E		N
	P	L	A	Y	W	R	I	G	H	T	S	

99

A: They're all reflexive pronouns: HERSELF, ITSELF, and HIMSELF.

B: 10D. The number represents the number of sides a shape has, while the letter is the initial letter of the corresponding shape: a Triangle has 3 sides, a Square has 4, Pentagon = 5, Hexagon = 6, Heptagon = 7, Octagon = 8, and Nonagon = 9. Next would be a Decagon (D), which has 10.

C
The word is PAPERCLIP.

```
R E S I S T O R   P E A K T O P E A K
A   G     A   U   U       A     I
D   B   M O D U L A T O R   R A I L
I   T   O   A   S   O       A     O
O   S   D   R   E   R   O   F L O W
F O U R I E R     C   E   H   O   A
R   B   M   M H O   C A M E R A   T
E   M       O   D   L       M     T
Q U A D R A T U R E B O O S T E R   H
U   R   E   S   M   S     R     O
E   I   E   R E M O T E       S   U
N O N O D E     D   R   F I L T E R
C   E   S   I N P U T     L     E
Y   C   W     O   L     A I R W A V E
    A   I     I   A M P   P   D L
R O B O T I C S   T   O   F   B Y T E
E   L   C     E   I   T   L   S   C
A   I   H   T R I O D E   O   T   T
L I N E     E   N   N   P   P A I R
T   G     L C D     T       T   O
I       I   U   S   I   P   N E O N
M E C H A N I C A L F A U L T
E   E   K   T   E   L   A   G O B O
  S U R G E   I   E     S   A
  N   T   R   O   V O L T M E T E R
  R   Z     N   E     A   E
```

Printed in Great Britain
by Amazon

57238418R00086